Accident!

Tessa Krailing

Nelson

Contents

Rocky's fall

On Saturday morning the kids who live in
Wellington Square went to the park.
They played football, flew kites and
went on the swings.
One Saturday morning Rocky saw
Jamila on the swings.
'Hello, Jamila,' said Rocky.
'You're not swinging very high.'
'I get scared if I swing too high,'
she said.
'I'm scared I might fall off.'
'You won't fall,' said Rocky.
'I'll show you.
Let me have a go.'
Jamila got off the swing and Rocky
got on.
He began to swing higher and higher.

Rocky was having a great time.
'Look at me!' he called to Jamila.
'I'm swinging much higher than you did.'
Rocky was standing up on the swing.
'You can swing much higher standing up!'

Jamila watched Rocky swinging higher and higher.
'Be careful, Rocky,' she called.
'You're swinging too high.
You'll fall off in a minute.'
'Don't be silly,' called Rocky.
'I know what I'm doing!'

Rocky laughed at Jamila.
'I'm not scared of falling,' he shouted.
But suddenly Rocky's feet slipped off
the swing.
He slipped and fell.
He had been swinging very high and
he fell a long way.
The ground was very hard and Rocky
bumped his head.
He lay very still.

Jamila screamed and ran over to where
Rocky lay.
'Rocky, are you hurt?' she said.
Rocky didn't move.
His eyes were closed.
His head was bleeding.
Jamila knew that she had to get help.
She couldn't see anyone in the park.
She ran off quickly to find Fred.

'Where will he be?' thought Jamila.

He wasn't by the pond or near the statue.

Jamila ran to the shed.

Fred was just having a cup of tea.

'Fred, come quickly,' called Jamila.

'Rocky has had an accident.

He's hurt himself.

He's bumped his head on the ground and he's bleeding.'

Fred put down his cup of tea.

He jumped up and followed Jamila across the park to the swings.

Rocky still had his eyes closed.
'What shall we do?' asked Jamila.
'Should we pick him up?'
'Don't try to move him,' said Fred.
'I'll call for an ambulance.
You go and get his Mum.
Be as quick as you can.'
Jamila ran out of the park.
Fred put his coat over Rocky to keep
him warm and then went to call the ambulance.

Where is Rocky's Mum?

Jamila went to Number 5 Wellington Square
where Rocky lived.
She banged on the door.
No-one came.
Jamila banged again.
No-one came.
She shouted through the letter-box.
Mr Crisp next door heard her shout.
'She's not in,' he said.
'Oh dear,' said Jamila.
'Do you know where she is?'
'I think she went to your Dad's shop,'
said Mr Crisp.
'I must find her,' said Jamila.
'Rocky has had an accident in the park.
He's hurt his head and he's bleeding.'

Jamila ran off to her Dad's shop.
It was empty.
Mr Patel was in the back.
'Dad,' called Jamila.
'Have you seen Rocky's Mum?'
Mr Patel came through to the front of the shop.
'Yes,' he said.
'She was in here about ten minutes ago.'
'Did she say where she was going?'
asked Jamila.
'No,' said Mr Patel.
'Why do you want to find her?'
'Rocky fell off the swing in the park,'
said Jamila.
'He's hurt his head and he's bleeding.'
'Oh dear,' said Mr Patel.
'Have you been to Rocky's house?'
'Yes,' said Jamila.
'I went there first but Mr Crisp
said she was here.
'I'll see if she's at home now.'

Jamila left the shop.
On her way to Rocky's house she saw
the ambulance come into the Square.
They must be taking Rocky to hospital.
If only she could find his Mum!
Jamila went back into the park.
PC Kent was talking to Fred.
'Did you find Rocky's Mum?' asked Fred.
'No,' said Jamila, looking unhappy.
'She's not at home and she'd left
the shop ten minutes ago.'
'I'll help you find her,' said PC Kent.
The ambulance was leaving.
Max wanted to follow Rocky.
'Look at Max,' said Fred.
'He wants to follow Rocky to the hospital.'
PC Kent picked up Max.
'We'll put him in my car and then
we'll look for Rocky's Mum.'
PC Kent and Jamila left the park.
He put Max in the police car and
they went to look for Rocky's mum.

They went back to Rocky's house but
she wasn't there.
'We'll go all around the Square,' said
the policeman.
'That way we are sure to find her.'
They went around the Square asking people
if they had seen Rocky's Mum.
Suddenly, Jamila saw her.
'There she is!' Jamila said.
'She's talking to Mr Miller.
Quick, let's go and tell her what's happened.'
'Better leave this to me,' said PC Kent.

Rocky's Mum was very upset when PC Kent
told her about the accident.
'I must get to the hospital,' she said.
'I'll take you there in my car,'
said PC Kent.
'Can I come too?' asked Jamila.
'Yes, I'd like you to come,'
said Rocky's Mum.
They all got into the car and
very soon they were at the hospital.

The hospital

Jamila had never seen inside a
hospital before.
'It's very big,' she said.
'How will we find Rocky?'
'He'll be in the children's ward,'
said PC Kent.
Outside the children's ward the doctor
came to talk to Rocky's Mum.

The doctor spoke very quietly.
'What is she saying?' asked Jamila.
'She says Rocky's Mum can go and see him,'
said PC Kent.
'But we must wait outside.'
'Can't I see him?' asked Jamila.
'Later,' said PC Kent.
'For now, only his Mum can go in.'

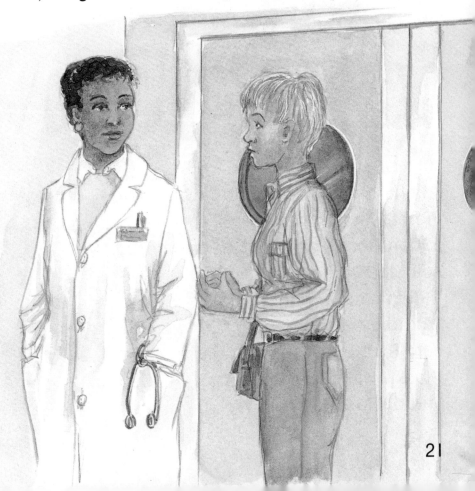

Jamila and PC Kent sat down outside
the children's ward.
'When Rocky was hurt I was scared,'
said Jamila.
'I didn't know what to do.'
'You did the right thing going for Fred,'
said PC Kent.
'Rocky will be OK now he's in hospital.
The doctor will look after him.'

The doctor took Rocky's Mum into the ward.
Rocky was in bed with his eyes closed.
'He looks so white,' she said.
'He's had quite a bump on the head but
he should come around soon,' said the doctor.
'Why don't you sit by the bed and wait?
He'll be pleased to see you when
he opens his eyes.'

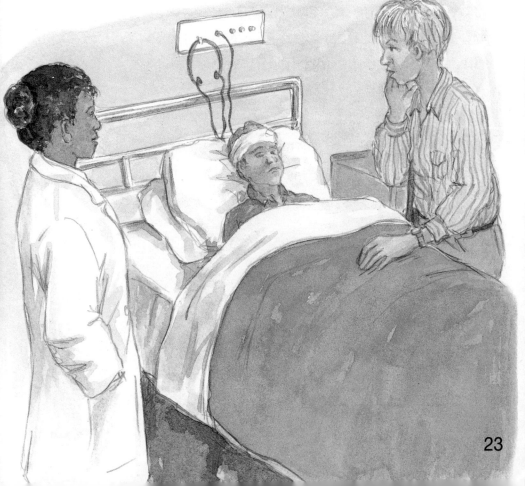

Rocky's Mum sat down by the bed.
She was still upset.
Rocky looked so white.
In a few minutes Rocky opened his eyes.
He saw his Mum by the bed.
'Hello, Mum,' he said.
'What am I doing in bed?'
Rocky tried to sit up but his head
hurt so much he couldn't.
'Don't try to sit up,' said his Mum.
'You fell off the swing in the park and
hurt your head.
You're in hospital.
But you can come home soon.'

Rocky's Mum came out of the ward.
PC Kent and Jamila got up.
'He's all right,' she said.
'His head hurts but he's all right.'
'Can he go home?' asked Jamila.
'Not for a day or two,' she said.
'The doctor wants to watch him for
a day or two.
Would you like to see him, Jamila?'
'Yes, please,' said Jamila.

Rocky's Mum took Jamila into the
children's ward.
They went over to Rocky's bed.
'Hello, Rocky,' said Jamila.
'Are you feeling better?'
'Not much,' said Rocky.
'My head hurts like anything!'
'You fell a long way,' said Jamila.
'And the ground was hard.
You were bleeding and your eyes were closed.'
'What did you do?' asked Rocky.
'I didn't know what to do,' said Jamila.
'I went to get Fred and he called for
an ambulance.
He told me to go and find your Mum.'
Rocky's eyes began to close.
'We'd better go now,' said Rocky's Mum.
'I'll be back later.'

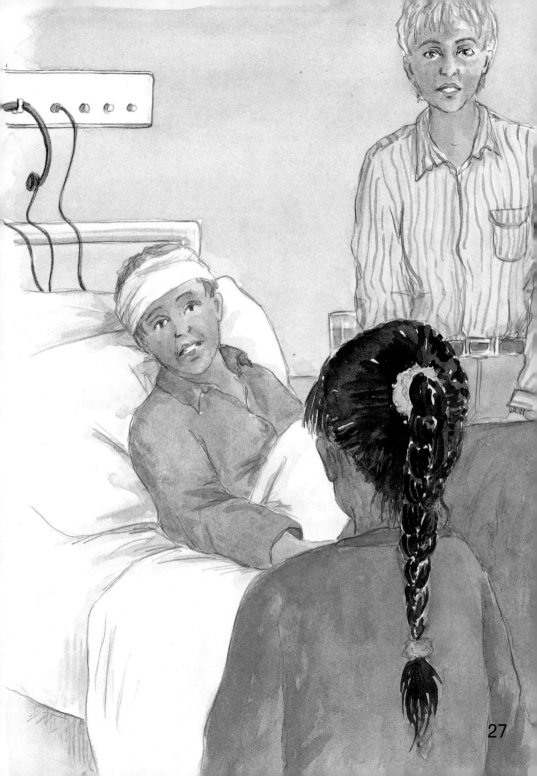

As they left the hospital Jamila said,
'I'd like to be a doctor.
Then I could help people when they got hurt.'
PC Kent took Rocky's Mum and Jamila back
home in the police car.
Max was still shut in the car and
he didn't like it.
He wanted to see Rocky.
'Rocky will be home soon,' said Jamila.
'You can see him then.'

Rocky comes home

Two days later Rocky left the hospital.
The doctor said that he could go home.
He was feeling much better.
His Mum came to pick him up.
'Now you don't want to end up in
hospital again, so be careful on the swings,'
she said.
'I will,' said Rocky.
'It was a silly thing to do, standing
on the swing like that.
I'm glad it's all over.
I can't wait to get home.'

Rocky was glad to see Max again.
And Max was glad to see Rocky.
The dog jumped up and down and
wagged his tail.
Rocky took him for a walk to see Jamila.
'Hello, Jamila,' he said.
'What are you doing?'
'I'm a doctor,' said Jamila.
'Next time you have an accident,
I'll know what to do!'
'There won't be a next time!' said Rocky.
'I won't be so stupid again.'

On his way home, Rocky went
to the park.
He sat on one of the swings.
He wanted to see if he was scared.
He began to swing.
Just a little at first.
And then higher.
It was OK as long as he didn't
swing too high!